The Moringa Manifesto

The Moringa Manifesto

*An Intensive Look into the History
and Future Uses of Moringa Oleifera*

Alonzo Fears-Dull

The Moringa Manifesto: An Intensive Look into the History and Future Uses of Moringa Oleifera

Jones Media Publishing
10645 N. Tatum Blvd. Ste. 200-166
Phoenix, AZ 85028
www.JonesMediaPublishing.com

Disclaimer:
The author strives to be as accurate and complete as possible in the creation of this book, notwithstanding the fact that he does not warrant or represent at any time that the contents within are accurate due to the rapidly changing nature of the Internet.

While all attempts have been made to verify information provided in this publication, the Publisher assumes no responsibility for errors, omissions, or contrary interpretation of the subject matter herein. Any perceived slights of specific persons, peoples, or organizations are unintentional.

In practical advice books, like anything else in life, there are no guarantees of income made. Readers are cautioned to rely on their own judgment about their individual circumstances to act accordingly. This book is not intended for use as a source of legal, business, accounting or financial advice. All readers are advised to seek services of competent professionals in legal, health, business, accounting, and finance field.

ISBN: 978-1-948382-39-7 paperback
Printed in the United States of America

*Dedicated to
my wife and my mother.*

ACKNOWLEDGEMENTS

I would like to acknowledge the hard work and commitment of Jeremy Jones and the Jones Media Publishing group. This project would still be an idea if not for the help of this amazing team. I would also give a special thanks to Mr. Zeeb for his years of service to the educational system and giving me the foundations of writing that I continuously use today.

FOREWORD

Before I begin this book, I'd like to give a special thanks to my wife who has started me on my journey into many life-changing habits which I've come to embrace today. She took her growing knowledge to create a beautiful garden in just under a year. We utilize many of her homegrown herbs and flowers for our own medical purposes, thus fueling my interest in promoting this incredible tree.

The purpose of this book is to further educate those who enjoy gardening and the many benefits of eating naturally grown crops and herbs. Over the past year I have found a particular interest in the Moringa Oleifera tree, and even though there are about 13 different species native to Africa and India, there are not many informational books on this miraculous plant. There are many organizations trying to promote large plantings and uses of this tree in the United States and worldwide. In the following pages, I hope to enlighten and inspire readers to not only use Moringa but to begin planting their own miracle trees.

Please note that all information collected here has come from articles posted on the National Center for Biotechnology Information and other articles published on the topic of Moringa. I encourage further research into the Moringa tree beyond this book. The information provided in this book is the tip of the iceberg of clinical testing and articles written; even the category of this plant is unclear. Some claim it is an herb and others claim it is a vegetable. The FDA has not evaluated any of the statements that will be made.

I am not a doctor, and this book is not intended to give medical advice to diagnose, treat, cure, or prevent any diseases. I encourage you, the reader, to consult with your doctors if you are pregnant, nursing or taking other medications to prevent any adverse side effects. The publisher and the author assume no liability for any injuries caused to the reader that may result from the reader's use of content contained in this publication and recommend common sense when contemplating the practices described in this book.

TABLE OF CONTENTS

BARE BASICS
OF MORINGA OLEIFERA

Moringa Oleifera (scientific family name Moringaceae) is a softwood tree with an astounding growth rate and is referred to by many names, including mulungi, drumstick tree, horseradish tree, ben (benzoil) tree, never-die, and the miracle tree. This genus is indigenous to sub-Himalayan parts of Northern India with altitudes between 1900-4000 feet (600-1200 meters) and has 12 other related species that grow in various regions of the world.

Currently, Moringa is most commonly found in Africa, Asia, and the Middle East; in recent years there have been garden enthusiasts who are promoting

Moringa growth in the United States. Moringa has an amazing ability to survive in dry, humid, and poor soil areas but it's been found in some cases not to thrive in clay soil areas or those that are waterlogged. Ancient records document Moringa seeds, branches, leaves, flowers, and cakes as being used for many things from skin care to gastrointestinal medication.

The Ayurvedic practitioners of natural medicines in India have identified more than 300 diseases that could potentially be cured using the different parts of the Moringa. Special mention is made about the psychological and spiritual properties that Moringa allows a user to achieve. They believe this powerful herb penetrates deep layers of the body's tissues and bone marrow.

Moringa has been used by Ayurvedic physicians to help bring clarity and body restoration to a person. A common belief is that Moringa has a powerful role in purifying the blood by removing toxins, impurities, parasites, and metabolic wastes. India possesses more traditional and scientific medical knowledge about Moringa than traditional Chinese medicine, due to these plants being introduced to China in the 1960s and not being considered a Chinese herb. Both traditional medicine practices in Asia promote the herbs as anti-inflammatory, antiparasitic, anti-hypertensive, hypolipidemic, hypoglycemic, having diuretic effects and aiding in a multitude of gastrointestinal, gynecological, and dermatological issues. African and Western medicine hold claims that Moringa can treat malnutrition, obesity, and has lipid-lowering properties. Leaves are attributed to act along the stomach meridian which also include the liver and spleen. With presentation of immunological properties, Western medicine speculates that Moringa could be an adequate and supportive therapy for those with a coronavirus infection when combined with Western medicine. Before you run out to buy Moringa instead of your next Z-Pack, please be sure to read Section 3 on the cautions to these speculations.

All parts of this tree, from its roots and seeds to its leaves and flowers, are edible, but caution must be taken once the tree matures as the bark and roots can be utilized for stronger medicinal purposes. Always consult your doctor before taking any supplements to find out if adverse side effects could occur with current medications or if you are pregnant or breastfeeding. Studies have found that many parts of the tree are suitable for not only human consumption but for animal consumption and may even serve as a possible source of biofuel in the future.

Moringa seed oil (Behen/Ben oil) can be created by cold pressing the seeds which preserves the nutrients and prolongs the shelf life, as opposed to hot pressing. Among the rural communities who have no machines, the edible oil is extracted by boiling the shelled seeds in water and collecting the oil by skimming it from the surface of the water. This oil can be used for cooking as well as to prepare biodiesel as lubricant. Around the world, many countries use Moringa seeds and seed cakes to purify their waters and implement the leaves into their traditional diets. The leaves are rich in fiber, proteins, minerals, beta carotenes (the major antioxidant converted by the human body into Vitamin A), and antioxidants. Moringa studies have also suggested that it carries anticancer, antibacterial, antidiabetic, antifungal, and anti-inflammatory properties due to the presence of bioactive compounds (chemicals that are found in certain plants and some foods that are thought to fight disease and certain cancers).

An in-depth comparison of 100 grams (3.5 oz) of dry leaf Moringa to other vegetables and foods shows the many nutritional benefits received from the tree in its various forms. Moringa leaf has the potential to have 7x more Vitamin C than oranges, 9x more protein than yogurt, 10x more beta carotene (Vitamin A) than carrots, 15x more potassium than bananas and 25x more iron than spinach. Research has even found that Moringa has less than 1 gram (0.03 oz) of carbohydrates in the powder per teaspoon.

What sets Moringa apart from other herbs, along with all these great benefits, is that it does not contain caffeine. Some users have reported only using the tea or capsules during the day because they experience an energy boost that keeps their mind awake, allowing them to accomplish more during the day. This effect could be attributed to the fact that the dry leaves retain 20%-25% of its nutrients while the dry powder retains up to 95% of its nutrients, if processed appropriately.

The oil is the main product of the seed and is approximately 36.7% of its total weight. In the future, we may even see Moringa seed oil being substituted for olive oil. Moringa seed oil has monounsaturated fatty acid contents, similar to olive oil, but there is a lower content of polyunsaturated fatty acids that may limit the oil's nutritional value. However, this lower content of polyunsaturated fatty acids, from a scientific standpoint, suggests greater shelf stability due to its high resistance to oxygen. In an article written by Diana Meireles in 2020, the following listings were documented on the traditional views and uses of Moringa of the Ayurvedics and in Traditional Chinese Medicine (TCM) where they used it for a multitude of physical and mental remedies:

Roots: Taste is acrid and bitter, Ayurvedics believed Moringa could aid in the following areas: abcesses, alexipharmic (antidote for poison), anorexia, ascites (abnormal fluid in abdomen), asthma, cardiomyopathy (structural disease of the heart), carminative (expelling gas from stomach, or flatulence), colic, coughs, diarrhea, dyspepsia (indigestion), fever, inflammations, renal calculi (kidney stones), and verminosis (infestation of parasites). They believed in the roots holding qualities such as: anti-inflammatory, diuretic, expectorant, stimulant and thermogenic. The roots were believed to have a grounding and calming sensation, causing the user to feel a sense of serenity and balance, aiding in clarity during times of uncertainty. Traditional Chinese Medicine recommends use for dizziness, flatulence, gastrointestinal issues, headaches, high blood pressure and skin issues.

Bark: Taste is acrid and bitter, believed to be abortifacient, antifungal, cardiac and circulatory stimulant and thermogenic. Ayurvedics also believed in using the bark to treat ringworm.

Leaves: Taste is bitter, found to be an anti-inflammatory, aiding in eye health, anodyne (alleviates pain), anthelmintic (destroying parasites) and rich in Vitamin A and C. Other uses were to fight scurvy, tumors and some wounds. Traditional Chinese Medicine claim leaves can be used for anemia to tonify the blood, and has an ability for reversing severe malnutrition, as well as expelling toxins.

Seeds: Taste is acrid and bitter, seeds can be eaten raw or cooked. Ayurvedics found seeds to be an anti-inflammatory, aiding in eye health, having purging effects and reduces fevers. Seeds were used medicinally for depression due to thoughts that the energy it gave the body could overpower the feelings of hopelessness. Traditional Chinese Medicine also used the seeds for people who have low appetites and bloating. Many of the phytochemical compounds isolated from the seeds can inhibit the growth of certain pathogenic microorganisms responsible for human infections.

Flowers: Ayurvedics believed that the flowers held more mental benefits. Practitioners would use the flowers to help a person clear their mind to let go of traumatic memories and heal emotional wounds and phobias. They had a belief that the flowers encouraged positive thinking and brought new insights to life. Additionally, the flowers were also a source of nectar and used to produce honey.

HUMAN HEALTH BENEFITS

From an herbalist standpoint, it is important to understand the effects of any herbs on the body, so be sure to speak to your doctor first before starting new products and be sure to ease into their usage. The various parts of Moringa are documented to act as cardiac and circulatory stimulants and to have antibacterial, antidiabetic, antiepileptic, antifungal, antihypertensive, anti-inflammatory, antioxidant, antispasmodic, antipyretic, antiulcer, antitumor, cholesterol-lowering, diuretic, and hepatoprotective properties. Studies have found that Moringa tea, Moringa capsules, and dried Moringa seeds stimulate brain functions, maintain blood glucose levels, restore imbalances in your diet, and regulate your gastrointestinal tract. There are testimonials that claim the use of Moringa powder and tea helps to regulate lactose intolerance, a PH balance deficiency in the stomach.

Moringa oil has been found to help skin appear younger and more toned; this could be attributed to the zeatin found in Moringa products. The Moringa herb contains a rare combination of zeatin, quercetin, beta-sitosterol, caffeoylquinic acid, and kaempferol. The properties that contribute to the improvement of the skin appear to be phenolics, zeatin, and antioxidants such as Vitamins A, B and C. Moringa extract creams have been tested for potential skin irritation through patch testing and have proven to be a nonirritant and reduces skin erythema (superficial reddening of the skin). Consistent use of Moringa oil has been found to remove wrinkles, clear pimples, tighten pores, and clear blackheads. Ancient documents detail using this oil on pregnant women's bellies to reduce stretch marks. Currently, many massage therapists and aromatherapists use Moringa oils with their clients for its calming attributes and cosmetic benefits. When made into a paste in traditional medicine, wounds were found to heal faster and, in some cases, even showed photo protective qualities (i.e. sunscreen). These medicinal purposes also include treating toothaches and potentially fighting gum disease.

The leaf combination of fatty acids, diuretic, lipid, and blood pressure-lowering properties also make Moringa a good candidate to maintain cardiovascular health. Many clinical studies are underway to find correlation between Moringa use and controlling diabetes. Diabetes is a condition in which the human body cannot produce enough insulin (the component that allows the glucose to be brought to the body's cells to use for energy) or the body's inability to use all the glucose that is made. Conventional medicines for glucose regulation targets other organs, such as the pancreas, to reduce glucose levels rather than the small intestines. Compounds that are found in Moringa appear to target the small intestine and reduce the ability to absorb glucose in some cases, helping it circulate the glucose properly in others. Type 1 and Type 2 diabetes need further testing, but there are some users who consume Moringa to regulate their insulin levels versus using the conventional diabetic medications. All testing that has been conducted have shown a promising future for the use of Moringa in diabetic treatment.

The Ayurvedic believe that Moringa influences users at an emotional, energetic, mental, and spiritual level. Moringa has been tested in scientific research and was proven to have anti-depressive and anxiolytic (anxiety reduction) effects; it is also considered an adaptogenic (aids body in adapting to stress), labeling it an anti-stress herb. Additionally, there have been case studies in which mice that were orally given Moringa showed a decrease in oxidative stress levels, promoting cognition and antidepressant activities.

Moringa tea has been studied and shown to create alterations in blood circulation which confirms the adaptogenic capabilities for relieving stress. There have also been reports of Moringa seed extract producing anti-inflammatory responses in certain diseases such as asthma and rheumatoid arthritis. These reports found the extract to alleviate broncho-alveolar inflammation by decreasing the infiltration of inflammatory cells into the lungs, reducing the secretion of inflammatory mediators into the airways of asthma-induced rats. Additionally, it has been reported that Moringa can be used in treating Irritable Bowel Disease and Lactose Intolerance due in part to its anti-inflammatory capabilities.

In tropical and sub-tropic regions (Africa, Asia, and some parts of North America and the Equator), Moringa is being advocated for use in HIV-positive people as an immune booster and nutrient supplement. It was reported by 80% of HIV-positive Moringa users that the main reasoning for consumption was for immune boosting effects. Others indicated they use it to help arthritis, diabetes, digestive disorders, hypertension, and nutritional disorders. Dosages are still under study, and it is not clear yet how to dose with body type, weight, existing conditions, etc. Users vary on dried leaf doses of Moringa that range from a pinch to one tablespoon, while the leaf powder is used either alone (41%) or in combination with the bark and/or root (37%). At this time, it is found that almost 70% of cases in which the herb was used came from users having the recommendation of use from a friend or relative.

In African and Indian countries where the Moringa tree has been used for centuries, the leaves are commonly used as substitutes for cabbage, spinach, and other greens. Complications of growing and purchasing at a market creates an issue for these countries and Moringa has been utilized to maintain steady nutritional value to its people. Research finds the phytosterols in Moringa promote lactation in female humans. Cases in Africa report that Moringa use has positive effects not only on those who are pregnant but on their children as well. Breast milk production increased and, in some cases, babies who had suffered from anemia were brought out of it with the use of Moringa through the mother's breast milk. There are even some cases documented in Africa as well as in America of Moringa being used to treat Sickle Cell Anemia.

The Great Debate: CBD or Moringa?

Recently, many Moringa and marijuana growers are trying to compare their herbal products. More specifically, many try to compare CBD oil, which is the most legal form of Cannabis products, and Moringa leaves/oil. In this section, we can dive a little into the similarities and differences.

Comparatively, most use CBD for its anti-inflammatory, anti-anxiety, joint pain, sleep aid, and inhibitors of tumor benefits. Both Moringa and CBD hold a multitude of health-related benefits and can be made into oils, capsules, and gummies for consumption. Both do not necessarily have a dosing chart but CBD users and Moringa users are directed to use the supplements as necessary until reaching desired effects.

CBD and Moringa begin to differ almost from their first stages of production. Cannabis is grown and can be utilized in different forms that cause psychedelic effects; CBD oil is processed by using butane, pressurized CO_2, and ethanol. This process removes the cannabinoids (THC) in the process and allows the "safe" product to be sold in many different stores. The World Health Organization has declared this product to be safe for consumption and does not have a maximum dosage suggestion, claiming the only side effects could be upset stomachs.

Moringa, on the other hand, can be all natural from seed to products whether it be oil, teas, or capsules. Moringa oil is simply made from the seeds being generally cold pressed then utilized in cooking, lubricants, etc. There has not yet been any study or confirmations on the consumption of the oil and how it would affect humans, but the tea and the capsules are a natural way to consume the herb. The World Health Organization does not have a claim on these products and, as of now, it is suggested to take caution if you are taking medications for blood pressure, diabetes, and thyroid disease. Concerns of how Moringa changes how a person metabolizes certain medications brings forth these suggestions and cautionary advice.

An overview of these two products suggests they could potentially work in tandem to increase health benefits. No current studies have been conducted to find out the effects of the use of both herbal remedies, but theory suggests that it can add more potency to the sleep aid side of the CBD oils.

A CAUTIONARY WORD

Throughout studies in the clinical world, Moringa has been found to be mostly beneficial to humans and animals. However, there are some side effects that should be mentioned to remain unbiased about these products. Some studies found that, when used with other pharmaceutical drugs, Moringa caused them to break down, potentially leading to liver failure or cirrhosis. Some researchers claim the opposite in that it may be helping the liver damage that is being caused by harsh pharmaceutical medicines. Other studies found that high doses of Moringa products could lead to nerve-paralyzing properties. Also, the stems, roots, and flowers could cause complications in pregnancy.

As with any supplement, it is important to carefully monitor its use and any changes that occur; in the case of any adverse side effects, users should cease taking the supplements and contact their doctor. However, in all cases mentioned above, the doses that were used far exceeded the amount that would be found in normal food consumption of Moringa leaves. Prolonged intake and high doses could lead to these toxicity levels; therefore, it is recommended by these studies that no more than 70 grams (2.4 oz) of Moringa leaf should be consumed daily.

Many are hesitant to suggest using this natural medicine as an alternative to any other traditional therapies, especially in Western medicine. The concern comes from natural herbs having their own unique chemical makeup that could potentially induce side effects or even inhibit other drugs that may be taken by the user, resulting in failing treatments. Unfortunately, due to limited clinical studies that have a controlled group of individuals, the influence of Moringa consumption in relation to nutrition, neural development, and any link to disease is unclear at this time.

While attempting to remain unbiased on human consumption, this section is based on the limited and sometimes anecdotal findings on this herb. From what was gathered, most of the health benefits and side effects for humans and animals are theoretical and would require further research to confirm consistent results. I cannot stress enough that it is always suggested when beginning a new supplement to take caution in how much is consumed. Monitoring your body and how it reacts to medicines is always the best practice. Even throughout the herbal world, mixing certain herbs together has benefits and side effects; it is the duty of the user to ensure they do their research and weigh the pros and cons of the medicinal path they wish to travel.

Environmental Cautions for Growers

While Moringa users should consume with caution, those who grow it also need to carefully observe the process. From the perspective of the trees generally growing in African, Asian, and European countries, there are different insects and diseases that are common to different areas. Be mindful of this when you begin your growing journey of Moringa. Even though Moringa does have natural properties that may act as disease and pest repellents, be sure to document any insect damage or signs of disease (discoloration, plant death, unusual growths, etc.) and contact your local Department of Agriculture to map out possible issues.

There have been reports of hairy caterpillars, ants, termites, grasshoppers, crickets, and a few other insects causing harm to the Moringa plants in the dry season. The affected areas are suggested to be treated with a solution of Neem seed oil and soapy water. Some believe planting a Neem tree next to a Moringa tree is best because they complement each other's growth. The Neem seed oil is also a proactive deterrent to any fungal diseases (i.e., Alternaria Solani, which is normally found in potatoes and tomatoes in the U.S.) that may occur in Moringa tree leaves, causing leaf browning and the bark to turn black. Practicing proper weed removal and preventative sprays will also help to ensure a healthy crop.

Always remember that good growing practices will ensure that your garden will be productive and healthy. Most states have a Department of Agriculture course for a very low cost that can be beneficial to understanding composting, health safety, and pathogen knowledge to ensure everyone stays safe. If you are a producer, be sure to be mindful of your products and do not use or distribute any products that are not safe for you or others.

ANIMAL HEALTH
AND PRODUCTION BENEFITS

Moringa has found its way into animal farms due to its antimicrobial properties. Farmers have been experimenting with the leaves as a dietary substitute for the antibiotics normally given to livestock. This is not only because of its antimicrobial effects but because it is eco-friendly, having not produced any dire side-effects. When used in rats, it was found to have positive effects on asthmatic rats by reducing their lung inflammation, reducing blood glucose levels, and increasing their breast milk production. This not only gives a foothold to claims of the natural remedy being a good alternative to current antibiotics, but it allows hope to give future generations proper nutrition for their offspring which may eventually end up being served to people. This could be the answer for organic farmers who are looking to stay within parameters of the USDA Organic Laws, but also keep up with the other farms that use GMOs to increase production.

As the human population increases, meeting the demands of animal products that are safe for humans to consume will be a dilemma for our future scientists. Scientists have started experiments on poultry by giving them fresh Moringa leaves, air-dried, and then ground into a fine powder and utilizing it as leaf meal. In this study, it was noticed that supplements of the leaf meal at .4 oz/lb. (12 g/kg) could increase pH, their capacity to hold water, and increased the muscle fiber diameter in the breast muscle of the studied chickens. Additionally, higher weight and density of the tibia bone in the chickens were reported. However, it appeared that the mass of eggs and percentage of eggs laid appeared to be lower. Some farmers have reported that the shells of the eggs produced by the chickens who eat Moringa appear to be thicker and sturdier, which provides some support that the feed increases calcium and protein content of the shells.

Moringa use among aquatic animals has also indicated that the leaves can improve their growth and physiology. The leaf powder supplement addition of 5% into the diet was found to effectively enhance immunity and controlled infection in Nile Tilapia, and at 20% addition to diet increased antioxidant activity and immune parameters of Rainbow Trout. Additionally, 15% added to the diet of Grass Carp increased their growth and immune responses. Preparation of the Moringa supplements consisted of mixing the finely ground powder in distilled water at 208.4 °F (98 °C). This separated the solids from the liquids and then the liquids were frozen and dried in -112 °F (-80 °C) to formulate extract powder and then the extract was kept at that temperature until its use. Moringa supplements were found to show favorable improvements in immune responses and to help fight infections. Users that have fish have reported that they crush dried Moringa leaves very finely and use it as fish food and their fish eat it very intently and appear to have shown significant growth increase.

In addition, Moringa pellets are being made for cows and horses to eat. No documentation is found at this time for the consumption of Moringa pellets by horses, but cows have been studied in a few cases. One case found that the production of milk by the cows was increased by 58% when fed Moringa along with their current diet. In Columbia, farmers use the pellets to help increase cow nutrition and weight gain. With more consistent studies of using pellets, Moringa could be considered a valuable feeding product for livestock. This could be the beginning of Moringa carving a pathway to organic farmers who are trying to keep up with the demand for more production but cannot use GMO products with their livestock. Organically grown Moringa could be harvested on site of the farm, processed as necessary into pellets, then fed to the organic livestock that would then be available for human consumption.

Based on the studies above, it should be noted that these cases were given certain specifications for testing. As with any study, multiple studies must be conducted to find results and prove or debunk hypotheses. Just as with the human ingestion of the Moringa leaf, if farmers are willing to try this natural alternative to antibiotics and growth stimulants, proper measurements and documentation should be done to ensure the benefits are consistent. A turning point in the standard versus organic farming battle could be coming in the near future if enough benefits can be consistently found in the research of not only uses for animals but for uses in crops as well.

MISCELLANEOUS AREAS
OF BENEFIT

In other areas of scientific studies, it has been found that Moringa can be used as a fertilizer extract to increase the growth rate, size and disease resistance of leaves and plants. There is currently a company in Florida that has created a formula passed by the USDA to use as a plant growth stimulant. This special formula was created with more of the minerals and vitamins already found in the Moringa tree, with additional natural growth hormones to increase the flavors and sugars of the fruits. Scientists have studied the use of root bark extracts, which are made using ethanol, methanol, and distilled water, and are said to have antifungal properties against Red Bread Mold and Black Mold that grows on trees and their fruits. Using more eco-friendly means involving Moringa to produce these anti-fungal sprays could soon be seen with the proper funding.

There are some low-cost ways to produce Moringa growth solutions mentioned later in the book that can be used, whether in developing areas or industrialized areas. In some cases, farmers are using the Moringa solution on their crops 1-2 times a week from sprout until harvest, resulting in increased vegetable growth rates by 20%-35%. Not only are farmers using the solution, but they are utilizing the seed cakes to place in the ground and enrich the soil along with their compost. One report found that using Moringa as a form of soil fertilizer helped crops grown in it by almost 50% more than other fertilizers used. Moringa does not stop there with its ability to be a multi-purpose plant.

Seeds that are ground into powder have also been studied. It has been found that it has great potential to purify water, removing organic compounds and heavy metals in the water. These studies are finding that the seeds could be a natural solution to reducing bacteria in the water which could help developing countries. Current articles do not have solid results on the specific number of seeds or seed cakes necessary for use in water purification, but it will differ depending on the quality of the water. Additionally, studies have been conducted on Moringa trees and their impact on purifying the air. One study finds that one person emits 705 lbs. (320 kg) of CO_2 (Carbon Dioxide) per year and it would take only two Moringa trees two years' time to absorb this level of CO_2. Furthermore, one vehicle emits 5070 lbs. (2300 kg) of CO_2 per year, and it would take ten Moringa trees again only two years' time to absorb these levels of CO_2. Due to its incredibly fast growth rates, growing groves of trees could cut down on the pollution in the air worldwide in as little as two years.

Based on the Moringa data that shows it can be grown in poor soil, suggestions are made that the oil can be produced as an acceptable biofuel. Biofuel is renewable energy produced from vegetables and plants that can be effectively mixed with current gas and diesel, resulting in a cleaner burning fuel source. Biodiesel does not contain sulfur compounds and releases lower amounts of hydrocarbons, monoxides, and other harmful gases into the atmosphere by almost 12% in some studies. Due to Moringa's stability and lack of oxidation over a long period of time in storage, it has become one of the most popular candidates for use in producing biodiesel. Potentially producing biodiesel with Moringa was the focus of a recent study conducted in Australia which reports that approximately 6680 lbs. (3030 kg) of oil can produce 264 gallons (1000 L) of biodiesel. Moringa does not hold any toxic properties like other vegetables that have been researched in the biofuel sector. Additionally, this biofuel can reportedly blend with current diesel and not mandate a change to current engines. Studies did show lower engine braking power and torque power of the engines; however, this can be compensated for by other means to maintain lower emissions into our environment.

With the constant rollercoaster of gas prices, this natural alternative to fuel would be a sight to see in the future if combined with solar car technology as well. With the race for farmers in the organic sector to keep up with farmers that use GMOs, Moringa could offer a level playing field. While organic farmers would grow the Moringa for human consumption and cosmetics, if it was necessary, the GMO-using farmers could also be growing Moringa in the industrial sector to use in studies and production of fuel and lubricants. This could be great from the standpoint that, even if dusted with pesticides and GMOs from the other crops farmers grow, the Moringa could thrive, and it would not interrupt their current business. Organic farmers and GMO farmers could grow Moringa trees and have a new source of income for either commercial and industrial production, or even simply a means to feed their current livestock. Either way, the proposition is to grow groves of Moringa that could be planted and harvested around the country and even worldwide in months due to its quick growth rate, and it would create jobs for harvesters and oil production technicians as it is a special process to create Biofuel.

PLANTING
YOUR OWN SEEDS

There are two traditional ways of creating one of these "Miracle Trees."

1. Cuttings
2. Sowing seeds

The first method is simply the use of a broken or cut branch during pruning. Once the branch has detached, it is simply planted into the prepared ground and a new root system will sprout. Moringa tap roots grow straight down; they will not be invasive to the grounds around it.

The second method is the conventional way of growing seeds which entails poking a hole in the seed before wrapping it in a wet paper towel (preferably bamboo towel paper). Once placed into germinating trays or a plastic bag, the seeds should begin to sprout within 1-2 weeks (if this does not occur, seeds will need to be replaced with new ones). However, the seeds can be planted 24 hours after they have been soaking in the paper towels; the goal is to allow the water through the outer shell for a bit to feed the softer seed inside. Preparation of the soil with azomite, perlite, compost mix, and worms can help make the ground extremely fertile to the seeds during growth. Generally, the soil pH levels should be between 5-9 for best results. The goal is to create a well-draining soil, so adding some sand may also be best to reduce the risk of root rot.

Planting the seeds may take some architectural prowess, but it may prove simple based on your needs or preference for growing Moringa. Typically, it is suggested to have 6-9 feet (1-2 meters) in between each tree if you are planting them in a square or triangular method. This planting method is best for full sized trees that can grow to be 15+ feet (4.5+ meters) if allowed. If one is more geared towards mass harvesting of the leaves, there is a style called intensive planting in which you could use a raised bed to plant a seed every inch (2.54 cm) away from each other. Typically, intensive raised beds hold about 100-200 trees and are harvested constantly and can be allowed to grow as tall as the grower will allow.

Do not forget that when planting these seeds, the depth of planting them is only about one inch (2.54 cm) under the ground, and the dense collection of these trees needs to be monitored to prevent any disease from starting and spreading. As mentioned before for the cuttings, it is always suggested to prepare your ground first with proper mulch, compost (vegetative compost is best), and red wiggler worms to produce healthy soil for these trees to grow (called vermicompost).

For intensive beds, it is suggested to use red wiggler worms because they stay at about 1-2 feet (30-60 cm) down and many intensive gardens are raised beds. For a larger tree orchard style growing in a field or lot, it is possible to use earthworms because they tend to bury themselves deeper (3-6 feet/91-182 cm). When cutting the branches, be sure to make a cut about one inch (2.54 cm) from the knot of the branch to help promote growth. Also, when cutting the branches or main stem, make sure there is a 45-degree angle cut that allows the tree to grow again and reduce the amount of water that will stay puddled on the branches. Having the clippers on top of the branch angling downward is the best practice for cutting. When harvesting the leaves of the smaller trees, the branches are small and soft enough to pull off by hand close to the branch it stems from. In some areas, cutting the main stem down to 8 inches (20.32 cm) twice a year helps to promote more growth. The term "popping the top" is used when Moringa are still growing and pinching off the tiny leaves at the tops of the plant to promote multiple branch growth is also a common practice.

Normal planting season is during the rainy season and Moringa seeds can grow and germinate without the help of irrigation systems. These root systems have a good ability at this point in the season to develop roots that can withstand droughts. However, if you are planting for commercial purposes, you can have irrigation drip systems installed to ensure leaf production throughout the year. Irrigation should be set to either water in the morning or at night to prevent any leaf damage during the day. When the tree begins to grow and blossom, their flowers are referred to as bisexual zygomorphic flowers and can measure up to less than a ¼" (0.6 cm) long and can be white or cream in color.

The Moringa tree flowers have a special build of five pale green sepals and five white petals; the flowers are highly cross-pollinated which means best success for mass production requires large numbers of insects. When harvesting the trees once flowers have bloomed, it is suggested to pick them and start their drying process; due to the limited number of flowers produced each year, this is the most valuable part of the tree. Benefits of harvesting the flowers is that the tree may now redirect its need to pump energy into the flower growth and focus on new growth of the leaves and flowers ready to bloom.

In addition to flowers, which can also be harvested for use for its many health benefits and in some places honey, the tree also produces bean pods. Immature bean pods are sometimes picked and sauteed similar to green beans and make a delicious addition to your dinner plate. Mature pods, however, become dry and brown at maturity and can split open, revealing the seeds, which tend to have 12-35 in each pod. The seeds are brown and have a unique hull with three white papery "wings." Some producers of Moringa products have started to utilize these "wings" for creating paper and alcohol, another up and coming use of the plant. A single tree can produce anywhere from 15,000 to 25,000 seeds; there are approximately 4,000 seeds in 2 lbs. (1 kilo). The early flowering varieties can produce pods within six months, while other varieties may take up to one year.

Please note that Moringa trees flourish best between spring and fall seasons. When the trees sense colder temperatures, the tree will go dormant and stop its production. Keeping trees inside of greenhouses is suggested to try and encourage year-round growth. Very few cases have been found where the trees still produced leaves through the winter. There are some growers who are currently working on trying to pollinate trees with the ability to withstand the winter months in hopes of creating a year-round flourishing tree.

Seed Varieties

Below are a few of the different varieties of seed that are available on the market. Note that some varieties of seeds are better suited for leaf production, while others are more suited for pod production which eventually would lead to oil production. Ensure that when purchasing seeds, they were not stored for more than a year as this could lead to loss of germination ability.

MOMAX3 seeds are a perennial, non-GMO, proprietary variety for seed oil production developed by Advanced Biofuel Center (ABC) of Moringa India. The developer claims it will yield the world's highest seed oil production, producing up to 40% oil content. This variety is characterized by having a 90% germination rate, a 15–20-year lifespan, bears its fruits within 4-6 months, and can be harvested twice a year as it can produce 5-9 tons of seeds per year.

MOL'E is another non-GMO developed seed by Advanced Biofuel Center (ABC) of Moringa India. These were specifically bred to reach only 3-6 feet in height to further yield the highest output for leaf harvesting in intensive planting settings. This variety is characterized by having a lifespan of 5-8 years, 5-7 harvests per year and, for an unknown reason at this time, an increase of protein content as the leaf goes from fresh (10%) to dry (22%) then to a powder (29%).

ODC3 is named after Oddanchatram, an area in the Indian state of Tamil Nadu. ODC is a preferred choice due to its reduced need for water and fertilizer as well as high yields of pod production and a longer shelf life than other seeds. These trees grow quickly and, potentially, after three months they will begin abundant branching which makes this a great choice for intensive planting. Recommendation is that every year it should be cut down to about 3 feet from the ground levels. This variety is characterized by having fleshy and flavorful fruits, flowering within 3-4 months and yields about 300 fruits per year.

PKM1 is a variety released in 1989 and developed from the Eppothumvendran area of the Tirunelveli District of Tamil Nadu. This bushy variety can be medium sized to dwarf sized, reaching a height of 13 ft (approx. 4 meters) in its first year. This variety is characterized by producing flowers within 3-4 months of planting and pods within only 6-7 months, producing 200-400 pods per tree and having a flexible form, reducing breakage and giving them an extended shelf life.

PKM2 is a hybrid variety that is higher yielding, released in 2000. PKM2 was bred to have more branching than the PKM1 variety which was found to be desirable for its easy accessibility of leaves and pods for harvesting. This variety is characterized for producing an average of 240 fruits per tree and a more flesh-filled pod (70% flesh), making it ideal for cooking, oil production, and suitable for many different growing systems.

Aqua-, Aero- and Hydroponics

Some growers have expressed their curiosity over Moringa's ability to grow in different mediums other than traditional soil. There are three types that I would like to spotlight in this book.

Aquaponics roots itself from the word "aquaculture" which intends to cultivate using aquatic animals. In this type of system, a pump is placed into the water and supplies the tank with fresh and nutrient water for the plants and the fish. The fish emulsion (byproducts of fish) is a common fertilizer used in traditional gardening as well for its nutritional benefits for the plant's growth. This version of growing creates a mini, almost self-sufficient ecosystem in which the fish eat food, then create waste which the plants use for growth. The water in the tanks may need to be filled with the pump system, but the sand and gravel placed in the tanks sift the water, naturally filtering it.

Aeroponics is a style of gardening that sometimes goes hand-in-hand with a hydroponic design but has a few minor differences. Plants grown with this method can be shielded from the outside elements of nature which can reduce the number of pests, disease, and even root rot that it could encounter in a traditional garden. In aeroponics, plants are built onto a structure that allows the roots to hang freely below while the crop grows above the platform it is in. This structure may mimic the hydroponic method, but instead of pumped water through pipes, there is a misting system that is piped underneath the structure that allows for the plants to get the nutrient-rich water.

On the other hand, hydroponics has gained the limelight in recent years with gardeners who cannot afford the land to plant gardens. The concept behind this method is to use PVC pipes and pumps to create a cyclical circuit that constantly moves water through the plants roots. In this water is a nutrient-rich solution that feeds the plant all that it needs to grow. UV lights, pumps, and PVC pipe give this method a jump on traditional farming due to its effectiveness of plant production while also saving money on the land and fertilizer. Hydroponics allows plants to thrive indoors, so many natural elements such as pests, bugs, and disease do not affect the plants. Also, the biggest advantage is year-round production of plants due to the natural seasons not having effects on the temperatures inside.

No matter the style of gardening that a person would like to pursue, all three styles mentioned above are great ways to cut costs, produce crops, prevent disease and pest infestation, and limit pesticides that may be in the outside air which would create a more natural product. There are cases that have been reported where Moringa are growing very well with all these methods. These methods are mentioned to encourage readers to perhaps try more than one of these different methods before dismissing the idea of becoming a small-scale gardener for their Moringa plants.

Some may be worried about the massive amounts of water that are pumped into the piping system below and carry concern that this may cause the Moringa to be waterlogged. This case of waterlogging happens when excessive water is placed on the soil and the water does not move, in which it then attracts bugs that could be carrying disease and bacteria that eventually end up in the water puddle and then into the plant. Moringa may be resilient to these diseases and bugs due to the nature of its antibacterial and antimicrobial properties, however, even this "Miracle Tree" cannot survive root rot that can come along with waterlogging. The filter, pumping, and misting systems mentioned in the three types of gardening in this section would allow for constant water flow to the roots of the tree and high concentrations of all the nutrients needed for growth.

I highly encourage readers to further investigate the styles of gardening mentioned throughout this section, from the traditional to the hydroponic, and choose a method that is right for them. You do not have to be a commercial, large-scale company or grower to reap the benefits of having your very own Moringa trees that may aid you in better health.

PROCESSES
AND RECIPES

Processes

There are a few processes that will aid in utilizing your Moringa trees and in simplifying ways to produce your own Moringa products at home. Of course, if you are interested in home production, Moringa can always be mixed with other natural herbs to make them more flavorful or increase the effectiveness of the medicinal properties.

Fresh Leaves to Dried Leaves: Fresh leaves can be used in salads or any dish as a topping or mixed in. Always be sure to harvest leaves before the leaves turn yellow; a light green color can indicate new growth or the turning cycle but still can be used. When trees are older and have thicker branches be sure to use pruning cutters to cut an inch (2.54 cm) above the knot of the tree and at a 45-degree angle, even when cutting the tree in half to harvest and lower its height. This practice promotes growth and, in the case of rainfall or water getting to the trunk or branches, the water will not sit in a rut on the tree and rot the tree. Smaller branch harvesting can be done by hand and detaching directly at the base of the young branch also helps in growth.

Some producers strip the branches harvested and others leave them intact for drying. Utilize the method that works best for your needs. Ensure that after harvesting the leaves, you use a soft soap wash in a bowl, such as grapefruit wash or grapeseed wash to remove any aphids or bugs that may be on the leaves, letting it sit for approximately 5-10 minutes. Depending on resources, using a 1% saline solution can also be used and leaves will need to sit in the solution for 3-5 minutes. Once the cleaning is done, it is important to rinse leaves and shake as much water off as possible. If there is an excess amount of water on the leaves, it could shrivel the leaves more than normal. Nothing has been reported as far as losing any nutrients if excess water shrivels the leaves. When harvesting for drying purposes, ensure that the harvest, cleaning, and setting into a mesh drying rack or dehydrator occurs within 24 hours of the harvest. This will ensure freshness and retain the most nutrients. Another important step to nutrient retention is to dry from temperatures of 100°F (37°C) – 130°F (54°C) for up to four hours in a dehydrator (allow 15 minutes for leaves to air dry before using this method) and 8-16 hours in a mesh hanging herb dryer.

Powder: When making powder it is crucial that all leaves in the mix are dried leaves, otherwise the fresh leaves will release their moisture, making it unsuitable for storing. The suggested method is to place the dried leaves into a Vitamix blender (or any brand of your choosing, or a mortar and pestle) and set it to grind at medium to high speed into a fine powder. This powder can then be placed into smoothies, drinks, spices, tea, and even capsules. Note that when you are using this form in tea, the powder does not dissolve as would hot chocolate or a drink mix, so be prepared for the powder to be consumed almost whole. The consumption of the powder is very beneficial since different methods of processing the leaves bring out different amounts of nutrients in the Moringa.

Tea: When steeping your tea, you can buy small, biodegradable bags in which to place the dried Moringa leaves and place in your teacups. This will not only allow you to make your tea in a cup easier, but afterwards the entire bag can go into your compost pile and add to your nutrients. For those who enjoy the tea immensely, it's suggested to buy a French Press and add desired dried moringa and other herbs and flowers if you want and then let it steep for 5-8 minutes. Once you have steeped the brew, pour it into a cup before adding your sweetener of choice; this will preserve the leaves to remain more natural when you use the loose-leaf remains in your compost.

Capsules: Depending on the size you are using, purchase capsules (gelatin or veggie) and then find the appropriate machine to create the capsules. Size 0 capsules are recommended to hold 500 mg to 800 mg, depending on the degree of tamping. Follow directions of the capsule machine and find your method for packing and tamping the powder for your use. When placing the powder in capsules, using a flour dispensing cup with a lever action can be helpful in getting any leftover stems from getting in the way during the encapsulation process. When first starting to use these capsules, it is recommended to start with 2-4 per day, broken into a twice daily schedule. However, everyone has a different body type and metabolism rate, and these factors could require a person to take more or less depending on the effects they are experiencing. There have been reports of people taking anywhere from 10-16 per day, depending on the ailment they were treating.

Oil: For oil production, there is the traditional way of boiling off the oil from the seeds and skimming off the oil. In this method, it is suggested to let the oil sit in a room temperature area for 24-72 hours (or more if desired) so that the water can evaporate from the oil. The current at-home-method of extracting the oil is to purchase a cold press oil machine and preheat it to 200°F (93°C), and have the oil stay at room temperature after pressing to protect more of the nutrients. Even though the machine reaches this temperature, the oil produced will still come out to room temperature, and without the machine heated the oil yield could be lower. Fill the machine basket with dried, shelled seeds; some people leave the shells on the seeds which can affect the oil yield. Fresh seeds will not work for this process and will affect the oil yield as well. Traditional producers of oil either shell the seeds by hand or place them in a bag and beat them with a stick. There are some companies currently working on designs for a seed shelling machine, but it is still in the developmental stages.

For personal production, the use of a Vitamix blender half full and on low variable speed works best. This method works best 30-45 seconds, since all the hulls are heavier, and the inner seed is lighter; the seeds float mainly to the top of the blender, successfully saving it from the grinding. Place the entire grind into the cold press oil machine and the oil yield appears to be just as much as if it were separated into only seeds. Also, note that the electric machines do not have a rotary function in the bowl on top so either manual stirring of the seeds or building a contraption to mix the seeds as they fall into the rod area is needed. Otherwise, the seeds could become stuck in the top bowl area and inconsistent crushing could cause the machine to not work properly or burn the product. Once the seeds have yielded oil, it is still a good practice to let it set for 24-72 hours (or more if desired) to allow for the oil and seed remains to separate. When the final separation occurs and the oil at the top appears to be clearer, you can bottle at your convenience. If you are a huge commercial grower, there are rotary oil presses that can be used and larger means of mechanical presses to break more shells at one time would need to be utilized. Be sure to follow the directions of those machines and, again, room temperature pressing and cooling of the oil is suggested. After this process of cold pressing, the leftover husks are referred to as seed cakes and have been mixed into the soil to add more nutrients or, in underdeveloped countries, used as a water purification solution. To date, it is documented that

50-150mg of seed/ seed cakes per liter of water are necessary to gain the effects of purification.

Water Purification: One of the most promising developments of the Moringa tree for underdeveloped countries is the process of water treatment, which is still under study. One documented method is to crush the seeds or seed cakes and add 50-150 mg to 4 cups (1 liter) of dirty water. After the water starts to show visibly clearer water, the seed cake and seed can be strained out, being cautious not to move dirt and other substances that have been pulled to the bottom. A second method suggests using two soda bottle caps full of the crushed seeds, which is an estimated 6 oz. Place the seed grinds into a two-liter bottle and add a small amount of clean water which will activate the seeds properties once shaken for approximately five minutes. Once this task is completed, the mixture is believed to be able to purify up to five gallons (approx. 3.5 liters) of dirty water. This, of course, is subject to how dirty the water is and it's suggested with this process to boil the water after collecting the clear water without disturbing the substances at the bottom.

Poultice: This method of healing is a traditional custom that uses an herb-soaked bandage compress that can be applied to wounds. With Moringa being a soft leaf and wood, you can lay out gauze bandages and remove any hardened branches and place the fresh leaf into the bandage and double over the gauze. If you only have powder or dried leaves, be sure to add hot water, use a mortar and pestle for mixing until a paste is made, then apply the paste to the gauze. Place the bandage with the herbs on the wound site and continue to wrap the gauze to the body part or area, changing it every four hours, three times daily. Moringa in this form has been known to treat cuts, burns, and even bed sores.

Deodorant/Creams: By mixing equal parts Moringa seed oil and Moringa powder with a mortar and pestle, a smooth paste can be made. This paste can be used in medicine as described above or it can be utilized as deodorant. Moringa that is used for deodorant can have other fragrances or essential oils mixed in to gain a desired smell while treating your skin with the Moringa benefits. Creams can be created by using other products such as shea butter or other fragrances to make lip balms, skin care balms, or medical pastes.

Herbal Mixtures: Herbalists constantly mix herbs together to aid and amplify their effects. If you wish to go in this direction, please be safe and do your research on each herb you have chosen. Some combinations of garlic bulb, beetroot and Moringa powder have been used to help regulate blood pressure. Some people have reported using Holy Basil, Olive Leaf Powder, and Moringa Powder to aid in hormone and allergy control. Purchasing herbal books and doing a trial-and-error method can be the best way to find out what can be combined with Moringa. Be sure to match Moringa with other herbs by understanding that it is considered a coagulant, so herbs that say 'do not mix with coagulants' should be avoided.

Animal Pellets: More for the commercial agriculture producers, using dried Moringa leaves for pellets can be used for animal feeding. Drying the leaves and then turning them into leaf pellets is a simple process that involves a medium to large electric, diesel or gas machine that can compact the crushed dried material into pellets to use for fish, chickens, cows, horses, and much more. Farmers who currently make their own pellets enjoy the cost effectiveness as well as knowing what is going into the pellets. Farmers, especially those who are trying to feed their animals a better food source, worry about the quality of the products they are receiving when pellets are ordered. Making their own pellets assures them the knowledge of what they are feeding their livestock as well as the ability to regulate the size of the pellets, as needed. If organic farming is your business, this is a great way to grow additional crops that both humans and animals can enjoy.

Plant Fertilizer: One method for producing a low-cost, safe, and effective plant fertilizer is to start with fresh Moringa leaves. For every cup of fresh Moringa leaves, mix with four cups (approximately 1 liter) of water and blend. If a blender is not available, place the Moringa leaves into a cloth and dip into the water multiple times and strain by squeezing it into the water. Once blended, strain out the mixture into another pitcher and add four additional cups (approximately 1 liter) of water to the pitcher. Finally, add one drop of organic dish soap to allow this solution to stick to the leaves better and act as a pest deterrent. When using this in larger quantities, add proportionately increased amounts of Moringa and water. Spraying this solution from a spray bottle or a backpack sprayer is suggested. If none are available, using a rag or brush to splash the solution onto plants is suggested. This solution is to be used 1-2 times per week, either in the morning or evening when temperatures are cooler, and the sun will not damage the leaves. This solution works on all crops, including other Moringa trees.

Recipes

The following recipes are the simplest ways to make a delicious on the go treat that is packed with great nutrients and are completely vegan-based. I have used these recipes and enjoy the convenience of being able to make them without preheating a stove and grabbing them quickly as I run out the door for work.

Vegan Moringa Protein No-Bake Brownies

- 2 ½ cups of pitted dates (loosely placed into cup)
- 2 cups of crushed organic graham crackers
- ¼ cup of Moringa powder
- 6 tablespoons of cocoa powder/ cacao
- 1 ½ teaspoons of pure vanilla extract
- 2 teaspoons of water
- ¼ teaspoon of Himalayan salt
- Coconut oil

Gather all ingredients and use a Vitamix or food processor to combine the dates, cocoa powder, Moringa powder, vanilla, water, and salt into a dough substance. This process may appear to make the batter dry but keep it this way and do not add more water to the mixture. Use a square, 8-inch baking pan that is lined with coconut oil. Press the graham crackers into the bottom of the pan, covering the entire bottom, and going up the sides. Place the mixed batter into the pan on top of the graham cracker base and press to distribute the dough evenly throughout the pan. If you would like to add frosting, follow the recipe below. If you would like to skip the frosting, place the baking pan with all the batter and base into the refrigerator for a minimum of two hours to solidify. Brownies can be left out at room temperature covered up to a day and will last approximately two weeks covered in the refrigerator.

To make a frosting: Place the following into a medium mixing bowl and stir until ingredients make a paste. Then place this paste on top of the brownie batter as frosting.

- ¼ cup of pure maple syrup or agave
- ¼ cup of cocoa powder/ cacao
- 2 tablespoons of melted coconut oil
- ½ teaspoon of pure vanilla extract

Moringa Oat Ball Snack

- ½ cup of steel cut oats
- 2 tablespoons of almond butter
- 1 ½ tablespoon of agave
- ½ tablespoon of Moringa powder

Gather all ingredients and a medium mixing bowl. Mix oats, almond butter, agave and Moringa powder together in the bowl. Once mixed thoroughly, gather a tablespoon of the mixture and roll it into a ball; these measurements should allow you to make about eight oat balls. Once completed, place the balls into the refrigerator for about 15 minutes to solidify. Oat balls can be left out at room temperature covered for a day and will last approximately two weeks covered in the refrigerator.

Moringa Pumpkin Ball

- 1 cup of pumpkin puree
- ¼ cup of Moringa powder
- ¼ cup of almond butter
- ¼ cup of almond milk

Gather all ingredients into a medium mixing bowl and utilize electric beaters to mix ingredients together. This process may take about 1-2 minutes to fully blend. Once blended, use a small scoop to scoop out batter and mold into a ball. Not only a great human delicacy but being all-natural makes this great for behind dogs to enjoy as well.

*Be aware that the treats are nice to have occasionally, and while I am not a veterinarian, be sure to monitor your animals' intake. This recipe is not meant to be a meal replacement. If you have questions, please contact your local veterinarian on amounts that should be consumed by your animals.

Moringa No-Bake Horse Treats

- 1 cup of rolled oats
- ¼ cup of Moringa fresh leaf
- 2 tablespoons of molasses
- 2 tablespoons of coconut oil
- 2 tablespoons of apple cider vinegar
- Estimated 2 tablespoons of water (Accommodate for desired solid consistency)
- ½ teaspoon of Himalayan salt

Gather all ingredients into a medium mixing bowl to mix either by hand or beater machine. Once ingredients are blended, the batter can be made into a flat cookie shape or small round balls.

*Be aware that the treats are nice to have occasionally, and while I am not a veterinarian, be sure to monitor your animals' intake. This recipe is not meant to be a meal replacement. If you have questions, please contact your local veterinarian on amounts that should be consumed by your animals.

CONCLUSION

I hope you, the reader, have reached a comfortable standpoint to decide on your personal use of Moringa. This herb has a multitude of different properties that could potentially address health problems, disease, vitamin deficiency, malnutrition, and could even become a leading natural resource in the world.

Of course, there is always a push for more studies to be conducted on this tree to hopefully confirm some of the benefits and side effects it has on humans. As your knowledge grows about Moringa, and how it can become an essential part of your diet, placing the word out there is crucial and testimonials go a long way with Moringa promotion.

Remember also that when you are buying your Moringa products, it may be cheaper to get it from online stores– but do your research on where the product originates. Local growers, even yourself if you have decided to become a grower of this miracle tree, have fewer steps in moving and storing the product which can preserve the nutrients. As always, try to support your local growers. They are growing to benefit their communities and the products they have will be packed full of the nutrients from your very own region, which is better for your immune system.

Moringa has ecological, economical, and nutritional benefits and the development of consumption, production, and research is crucial to help every country's population.

REFERENCES

Abidin, Zaenal et al. *"Moringa oleifera* Leaves' Extract Enhances Nonspecific Immune Responses, Resistance against *Vibrio alginolyticus*, and Growth in Whiteleg Shrimp *(Penaeus vannamei)*." *Animals: an open access journal from MDPI* vol. 12,1 42. 26 Dec. 2021, doi:10.3390/ani12010042

African Journal of Food Science and Technology (ISSN: 2141-5455) Vol. 5(5) pp. 125-128, May, 2014 DOI: http:/dx.doi.org/10.14303/ajfst.2014.041

Anwar F, Latif S, Ashraf M, Gilani AH. Moringa oleifera: a food plant with multiple medicinal uses. Phytother Res. 2007 Jan;21(1):17-25. doi: 10.1002/ptr.2023. PMID: 17089328.

Christian K. O. Dzuvor, Sharadwata Pan, Charles Amanze, Prosper Amuzu, Charles Asakiya & Francis Kubi (2021): Bioactive components from Moringaoleifera seeds: production, functionalities and applications – a critical review, Critical Reviews in Biotechnology, DOI: 10.1080/07388551.2021.1931804

Dauphin, Cheryl. "A No-Bake, Healthy Horse Treat to Love!" *EquiGroomer*, Cheryl Dauphin   Https://Equigroomer.com/Wp-Content/ Uploads/2017/04/whiteLogo_rev-300x119. Png, 23 Oct. 2021, https://equigroomer. com/a-no-bake-healthy-horse-treat-to-love/.

Leaf for Life. "How to Make Moringa Growth Stimulant Spray." *How to Make Moringa Growth Stimulant Spray*, https://www.leafforlife.org/how/ moringa-growth-stimulant-spray/index.html.

Leone, Alessandro et al. "Moringa oleifera Seeds and Oil: Characteristics and Uses for Human Health." *International journal of molecular sciences* vol. 17,12 2141. 20 Dec. 2016, doi:10.3390/ijms17122141

Mahfuz, Shad, and Xiang Shu Piao. "Application of Moringa (*Moringa oleifera*) as Natural Feed Supplement in Poultry Diets." *Animals: an open access journal from MDPI* vol. 9,7 431. 9 Jul. 2019, doi:10.3390/ani9070431

Maurya, Vaibhav Kumar et al. "Fate of β-Carotene within Loaded Delivery Systems in Food: State of Knowledge." *Antioxidants (Basel, Switzerland)* vol. 10,3 426. 10 Mar. 2021, doi:10.3390/antiox10030426

Meireles, Diana et al. "A review of properties, nutritional and pharmaceutical applications of *Moringa oleifera:* integrative approach on conventional and traditional Asian medicine." *Advances in Traditional Medicine*, 1–21. 17 Aug. 2020, doi:10.1007/s13596-020-00468-0

Monera, Tsitsi Grace, and Charles Chiedza Maponga. "Prevalence and patterns of *Moringa oleifera* use among HIV positive patients in Zimbabwe: a cross-sectional survey." *Journal of public health in Africa* vol. 3,1 (2012): e6. doi:10.4081/jphia.2012.e6

Mulugeta, Getachew, and Anteneh Fekadu. "Industrial and Agricultural Potentials of Moringa." *Journal of Natural Sciences Research*, 2014, https://www.iiste.org/Journals/index.php/JNSR/article/view/14301.

Optimal, Every Day. "Comparing CBD vs Moringa: Benefits, Uses and More. Which Is Best?" *Every Day Optimal CBD,* 18 Nov. 2021, https://edocbd.com/cbd-vs-moringa/.

Parr, Larry. "How to Use Moringa Seed." *HomeSteady*, 14 Feb. 2019, https://homesteady.com/12427294/how-to-use-moringa-seed. (*Note this is a Blog)

Saint Sauveur, Armelle de and Broin, Melanie. 2010. Growing and processing moringa leaves. Moringa Association of Ghana (MAG), Accra, Ghana

Tittac. "Major Difference between Hydroponics, Aeroponics, and Aquaponics." *Tittac*, Tittac, 2017, https://tittac.com/en/what-is-the-difference-between-hydroponics-aeroponics-and-aquaponics#:~:text=While%20in%20aeroponics%2C%20the%20plants,free%20from%20pests%20and%20diseases.

"Varieties and Ecotypes of Moringa Oleifera." *Sustainablebioresources.com,* Sustainable Bioresources, 17 Dec. 2021, http://sustainablebioresources.com/plants/plant-families/moringaceae/moringa-oleifera/varieties-ecotypes-moringa-oleifera/.

Vargas-Sánchez, Karina, et al. "Effects of *Moringa Oleifera* on Glycaemia and Insulin Levels: A Review of Animal and Human Studies." *Nutrients*, MDPI, 2 Dec. 2019, https://www.ncbi.nlm.nih.gov/pmc/articles/PMC6950081/.

Veta, and Rod. "Recipes." *Moringa Farms*, Moringa Farms, 2 June 2020, https://moringafarms.com/category/recipes/.

ABOUT THE AUTHOR

Alonzo Fears-Dull is a local Arizona business owner who started his business after experiencing benefits from his own Moringa products. Pursuant to his own research on Moringa, he realized that there is a scarcity of centralized information available for the public to easily access and learn about this miraculous tree. He holds certification in organic farming and food safety because he has a high standard for his own Moringa business to provide and ensure that everyone safely uses the plant. He understands the struggles of farmers who strive to produce good, wholesome foods that are naturally grown and the consumer who wants naturally grown food for health benefits.

Spreading the knowledge of safe practices on how to use the different parts of the Moringa Tree is crucial for the worldwide use of Moringa Oleifera. Alonzo believes the Moringa Tree is nature's answer to helping the entire world – from animals to humans, and even other plants.

Thank you for reading *The Moringa Manifesto*.
We hope to have brought you new insight
to this miraculous plant. Please don't forget
to leave a review or comment with your
thoughts on the book, or even
testimonials for processes
tried in this book.